Tate

and His Historic Dream

Bernard C. Turner and Michelle Duster

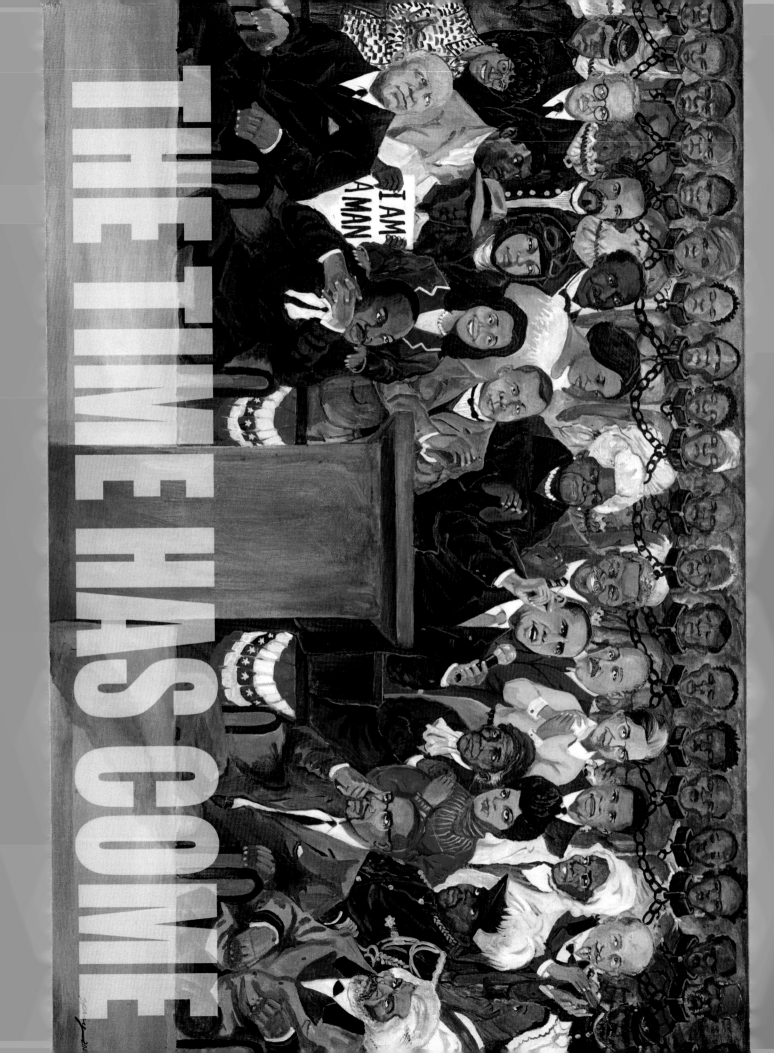

Tate and His Historic Dream

Bernard C. Turner and Michelle Duster

"The Time Has Come" painting by Derrell Spicy

Copyright © 2015 by Highlights of Chicago Press

ISBN: 978-0-9710487-8-2

Library of Congress Cataloging-in-Publication data is available on request.

HIGHLIGHTS OF CHICAGO

4325 N. Central Park Ave

Chicago, IL 60618

www.highlightsofchicago.com

e-mail: bturner@highlightsofchicago.com

Illustration, Graphic Design and Cover

Jennifer D. Turner

Ok To Dream, LLC

www.ok2dream.net

773.706.6632

History Consultant, Charles E. Duster, Jr.

Note from the Artist

I was always intrigued by history and had great admiration for several people who made a difference. I was inspired to create a painting that showcased people from different time periods who all worked to help our country get closer to what the founding fathers had in mind—a land that allows liberty and justice for all. I wanted to include both men and women, younger and older, who worked in a variety of professions in order to show the different ways people contributed to our country. My hope is that this painting "The Time Has Come" helps people learn about our history and think about the many ways that people have worked to make our country what it is today.

 Derrell Spicy

Note from the Authors

This story of Tate was inspired by the painting "The Time Has Come" by Derrell Spicy. In addition to finding the painting to be beautiful, we also realized that there was quite a bit of collaboration, rivalry, influence, and inspiration between the people included in the painting. We felt that giving voice to history-making people would make the history come alive in a unique and fun way.

Both adults and children alike should feel like they are on a journey with Tate as he meets the brave people who dared to challenge the status quo. Our hope is that the information presented in our book will peak curiosity and increase the desire to learn more about these great historic figures.

This book is dedicated to our parents and all of those who gave so much of themselves in the struggle for freedom and justice.

 Bernard C. Turner and Michelle Duster

Tate had a big dilemma. All of his classmates were finished with their Black History Month papers but him. He loved school and thought everything about fourth grade was really fun, except history. Who cares about these people who lived hundreds and thousands and gazillions of years ago? They're all old anyway, he thought as he sat at the kitchen table trying to begin his homework.

"Tate," his mother said. "You can't go outside and play until you finish your history paper." He looked out the window at the bright sunny day and knew his friends were in the park practicing wheelies on their bikes.

Tate slumped more in his chair. He didn't know how he was ever going to finish his paper, especially because he hadn't even started it yet. His teacher gave him the assignment over a week ago, but Tate kept putting it off so long that he only had one more day to finish.

He needed to write a paper about one of the people in the picture in his book. Tate stared at the picture trying to decide who would be the easiest to write about. This is torture, he thought. Why can't I just ride my bike today?

"Tate. Have you chosen who you'll write about yet?" his mother prodded.

"Not yet. I'm still thinking," he said. He fought off tears as he put his head on the book. I'm never going outside, he pouted.

The next thing he knew, Tate was standing on a platform in the middle of what seemed to be a town square. Suddenly he heard clanking sounds. He looked down the block and saw a group of black men who were chained together walking in a group.

His eyes widened with shock as he saw the black men lined up on the platform. The chains were taken off, and then a well-dressed white man walked across the platform as he looked at the men. Tate heard a voice offering money for one of the black men. That's when he realized that these men were slaves! After a few minutes, one of the black men was led away by another white man.

Tate couldn't believe that he was witnessing a slave auction. He never knew how cruel this could be and wondered where the man would be taken and what his life would be like. His teacher had told the class that people were brought from Africa to the United States in the slave trade for almost two hundred years, from 1619 – 1808.

Tate left the platform and started walking around the town square. He looked inside a window and saw a small woman wearing a bonnet. She was holding a quill pen and seemed to be deep in thought. He wandered into the door and said "Hello ma'am. Who are you?" He looked around the room thinking he would see his mother.

"I'm Phillis Wheatley," the woman said in a voice barely above a whisper.

Tate looked at the paper that was a lot bigger than what he used at school. "Are you writing a paper for school, too?" Tate asked as he got closer to her.

"No. I have never been to school before. I'm working on another poem. I'm lucky to be able to read and write."

"Why are you lucky to do that?" asked Tate. "Everyone knows how to read and write."

"Not slaves. It was against the law for us to become educated," said Phillis Wheatley.

"So, if you couldn't go to school, how did you learn how to read and write?"

"After I was brought here as a slave from Africa, I learned how to read and write from my master."

"What do you mean, after you were brought here from Africa? Were you sold as a slave, the same as those other people I just saw?"

"Yes. A man named John Wheatley bought me. I was so scared and lonely."

"Where were you born?"

"I don't remember. I was born around 1753 and was brought to

Boston in 1761 when I was about eight years old. I never saw my parents again, even though I lived until 1784. I was so sad that I spent my time writing."

"How does writing help you when you're sad?"

"It just does. I wrote my first published poem in 1770, and then I had a chance to go to England because of my writing. In 1773 my first whole book of poems was published."

"That's right, Tate," chimed in a booming voice from a man who entered the room. The tall man had shocking white hair. "This woman, Phillis Wheatley, is one of the best poets ever. And she learned how to read and write despite the obstacles. Those of us who were slaves didn't have the opportunity to go to school. You're very lucky to be able to do that. I had to sneak and learn on my own and pretend to not know anything."

Tate looked at the man and couldn't believe what he was hearing. It was a ridiculous idea that people didn't have the chance to go to school. Everyone did that. In fact, he knew people who refused to go to school and people had to force them to do it.

"Are you Frederick Douglass?" asked Tate, looking at this distinguished man who was dressed so formally in a three-piece suit.

"Yes, that's my name. How do you know who I am?"

"You're in my history book. Were you born a slave, too?

"I was born a slave around 1818 and died in 1895, but I spent a lot of my life fighting to end slavery and making sure that people after me had the opportunity to become educated," said Frederick Douglass.

"Well. I know slavery was hard, but now we can be anything we want to be," said Tate.

Tate heard someone else enter the room from behind him. "That wasn't always the case," said a man who had a cardboard sign over his chest with the words "I AM A MAN" printed on it.

Tate was totally confused. "What's the sign for?" he asked. "Everyone can see that you're a man."

"I'm a man, but I'm not treated like a man," said the Protester. I don't have the same rights and opportunities as a white man. I live in Memphis, Tennessee and work for the sanitation department. In 1968 they didn't want to give us equal working conditions or equal pay. We were just tired of it, and finally decided to go on strike. It was time to be treated like a man."

"But I thought that slavery ended way before 1968."

"Slavery ended in 1865 - over one hundred years before 1968, but in the 1960s we were still dealing with some of the same things that caused the problem to begin with. Let me tell you something," the

Protester continued, "slavery was such an issue in the United States that it caused a problem between the North and the South. Many southerners felt that slavery was good for the country. They felt so strongly about slavery that they decided to break away from the Union."

"What do you mean, break away?" asked Tate.

"The southern part of this country wanted to keep slavery as a way of life and they were ready to leave the United States and start their own country."

"You mean there could have been two different countries instead of one?" Tate was confused.

"Yes. The Civil War that was fought between the North and South of this country started in 1861, one year before I was born," said a woman who had on a red dress. "I was born a slave in 1862 in Holly Springs, Mississippi."

"Who are you?" Tate asked as he looked around the room. More and more people were starting to enter the room. He felt like he was at a family gathering. Tate noticed that the people looked like those in his book.

"My name is Ida B. Wells. And if it weren't for the Civil War, I might have been a slave all my life. Instead, because the North won the war, I became free when I was only three years old," she said it a quiet, yet firm voice. "I started my career as a teacher in rural Mississippi. I moved to Memphis and one day in 1884 I was asked to leave the ladies coach of a train to sit in the "colored" car. When I refused, I was thrown off the train. It was so humiliating that I decided to sue the railroad."

"What do you mean, sue the railroad?" Tate didn't understand.

"I filed a lawsuit against the railroad based on the fact that the train cars were separate, but not equal."

"I didn't know you could do that."

"Yes. It's important to stand up for your rights. I also decided to write about the injustice that I was seeing all around me," said Ida B. Wells.

"So you wrote stories?"

"No. In 1892 I started an anti-lynching campaign through newspaper articles, because even though black people were no longer slaves, we were being terrorized by mobs. I couldn't help myself. I had to speak up and write newspaper articles about what was happening to people in my community."

"You are lucky," said a woman who was wearing a blue dress with white ruffles around the neck. "I was born a slave in 1820 in Dorchester County, Maryland and had to escape from slavery because it was so bad. It was a very hard life and I just couldn't take it anymore."

"But how did you get away?" asked Tate.

"I escaped to Philadelphia in 1849. I wanted others to enjoy the freedom I felt. Before I died in 1913 I ended up going back to the South many times and led hundreds of people through the Underground Railroad to freedom."

"What's your name? Did you actually run a train for slaves?"

"My name is Harriet Tubman. And no, Tate, the Underground Railroad was not a train. It was a path that used secret codes and safe houses to help lead slaves to freedom."

Tate couldn't believe what he was seeing. All of these people who were part of a picture in his book were actually talking to him. They were real! They had voices and interesting stories to tell. Wow! If only my friends could be here to see this, Tate thought. They'll never believe me when I tell them that I got a chance to meet these people.

"I was born a slave too," said a woman who wore an all-white outfit. I had to make sure that people knew how slaves were treated. I started speaking about it."

"What's your name?" asked Tate. "You spoke out against slavery, too?"

"I'm known as Sojourner Truth. I was born Isabella Baumfree in 1799 and was a slave until 1827 when I was freed because of the New York State Emancipation Act. In May 1851, I gave a speech called "Ain't I a Woman" at a suffrage meeting in Akron, Ohio. I lived until 1883 and spent almost 40 years speaking about abolition and the rights of women."

"What is suffrage?" Tate had never heard that word before. Meeting these people made him feel like there was so much that he didn't know. Now he really wanted to keep going to school so he could continue to learn more.

"Suffrage is the right to vote," said Ida B. Wells.

Tate was confused. He thought that the Civil Rights Movement started with Martin Luther King, Jr. He had heard Dr. King's "I Have a Dream" speech on TV. He thought that there was just a dream about people being judged by their character and not by the way they looked.

"But, I thought Dr. King was the one who fought for civil rights," said Tate.

"I did fight for equality, son," said Dr. Martin Luther King, Jr. "There was a lot of injustice going on in the South during my time and it had been going on for almost 90 years when we organized that bus boycott in Montgomery, Alabama in 1955."

"But I thought Ms. Rosa Parks refused to get off the bus," said Tate.

"I did refuse to get off that bus," said Rosa Parks, who was wearing a yellow dress. Her gray hair was pulled into a bun and she

 wore wire-framed glasses. "I was just tired after working all day. And the thing is that I wasn't even sitting in the "White" section of the bus. I was already in the "Colored" section when the white bus driver asked me to get up for a white man because there were no seats available in the "White" section."

Wow, thought Tate. A white man asked a black woman to give up her seat? His grandmother had always told him that men were supposed to give their seats to women. He never heard that a woman should give her seat to a man.

How could the Civil Rights Movement start in 1955 if the Civil War ended in 1865, Tate pondered. Why didn't people have rights when they got their freedom after the Civil War ended? He needed to talk to some more of these people.

Information that he had learned in class was starting to become more clear to Tate. He remembered that during the Civil War there were two armies that fought against each other. The Union Army fought for the North and the Confederate Army fought for the South.

Rosa Parks said, "You know Tate, the fact that I could get on that bus at all is because of the fights that so many people had before me."

"We owe a lot of respect to the men who served in the Union Army," Rosa Parks continued. "Frederick Douglass gave a famous speech in 1863 where he urged black men to join the Union Army.

Escaped slaves and those already free went north to join the U.S. Colored Troops."

"I certainly felt that freedom was important enough to fight about," said Frederick Douglass. "But there were all kinds of ways that people helped with the war besides fighting. There were over 200,000 people who served as scouts, spies, blacksmiths, nurses, cooks and guides."

"I was one of the scouts!" said Harriet Tubman. "I also helped out as a nurse and a spy. Yes, sir. I was willing to do whatever I could to help gain freedom."

"A whole lot of us were," said Sojourner Truth.

"Didn't you also help in the war?" asked Harriet Tubman.

"I sure did," said Sojourner Truth. "I raised money for the soldiers and served as a nurse in the Civil War."

"I didn't know that women helped with the war," said Tate.

"Of course women helped with the war. Women have been involved in every part of this country's history," said Sojourner Truth.

"There was no way we could sit by and not help in the fight for the right to be free," said Harriet Tubman.

Wow. I can't imagine what it must have been like to not be free, Tate thought. He turned to the man who was wearing a blue army uniform and asked

11

"Did you fight in the Civil War?"

"Absolutely. I served as one of the colored troops in the army," said the Union Soldier. "There were more than 180,000 black men who enlisted in the Union Army in 170 regiments during the course of the Civil War. Close to 19,000 blacks served in the navy as well."

"I also fought in the war. I became a captain of the first official militia of colored soldiers in the Union Army," said a man with a jacket with lots of gold buttons on it. "I was born in Macon, Georgia in 1837, but lived in Virginia, Mississippi and spent a great deal of time in Cincinnati, Ohio."

"Wow! What's your name? I didn't know they had black officers in the Civil War," said Tate.

"My name, young man, is Captain Pinckney Benton Stewart Pinchback. After the war ended, we did a lot of amazing things with our freedom," he paused. "The outcome of the Civil War made it possible for many black people to get involved in so many things that weren't possible under slavery. I actually got into politics and became a state senator in Louisiana in 1868. Then, as a result of several twists and turns in politics, I became the first black governor of the state of Louisiana in 1872."

"So, you spent the rest of your time in politics?" Tate needed to know.

"Not really. I was interested in doing whatever I could to help us progress as a people. I started a weekly newspaper called the *Louisianian*, which I published for 11 years, and also became one of the founders of the American Citizens' Equal Rights Association and its first president." Pinchback continued. "This was one of the first attempts to form a civil rights organization with an agenda that would benefit the entire black population. A lot of progress was made before I died in 1921."

"Well, Captain Pinchback, thanks for your willingness to fight for our freedom," said a clean-shaven man wearing a blue suit with a black bow tie.

"Are you Booker T. Washington?" Tate asked as he tried to appear confident.

"Yes I am. I'm really impressed that you know me, young man."

"Well, I learned a little about you in my history class. But not much. Did you fight in the war, too?"

"No. I was too young to fight in the war," said Booker T.Washington. "I was born a slave in Franklin County, Virginia in 1856, and I got my freedom when I was 10 years old. I spent my life trying to figure out ways for blacks to become self-sufficient. I was so determined to make it possible for people to get an education that I founded Tuskegee Institute in 1881."

"Wow! You started a whole school? That's amazing," said Tate as he thought about how hard it was just to write one paper. "Why did you start a school? It seems like it would be really hard to do that."

"I wanted to teach people skills that would give them the ability to find employment or start their own businesses."

"School is the difference between having great opportunities and maybe spending a lifetime doing a lot of hard physical labor," said a medium-brown-skinned man wearing a bow tie.

"Are you friends with Booker T. Washington?" asked Tate.

"Yes. My name is George Washington Carver. I was born in 1864, the year before the Civil War ended. I took advantage of the opportunity to become educated and decided to become a scientist and educator. Mr. Booker T. Washington asked me to teach at Tuskegee Institute in 1896."

Tate felt like his head was spinning. He was trying to keep all of these people straight. He couldn't believe that some of the people in his picture actually knew each other. No one told him that in his history classes. Talking to these people was much more interesting than just reading about them, thought Tate. He had to find out more. "So, the two of you, Booker T. Washington and George Washington Carver, actually worked together?"

"Yes," said George Washington Carver. "I worked at Tuskegee Institute in 1896 and taught farmers about the necessity of replenishing nitrogen in the soil by rotating the crops. I also discovered many uses for the peanut, including dyes, glue, marble, printer's ink, and more. Uses for the sweet potato and pecans included glue, vinegar, synthetic rubber and material for paving highways. Many of the products developed were also used by the U.S. Army in World War I."

"Wow! I was only four years old when Mr. Carver worked at Tuskegee! I was born in Atlanta, Texas in 1892," said the woman who was wearing a soft helmet-looking thing on her head. Tate had never seen anything like that before.

"What's your name? Were you born a slave, too?" Tate asked.

"My name is Elizabeth "Bessie" Coleman. Have you ever heard of me before?"

"No. Not really. Is that a hat you're wearing on your head?" Tate couldn't help but ask.

Bessie Coleman laughed. "No, Tate. This is a helmet that I wore when flying my planes."

"You flew planes? I didn't know black women were pilots back then."

"I was the first black woman licensed to fly a plane. A huge part of the reason I got so interested in flying is because my brother

15

was a veteran of World War I," said Bessie Coleman. "At the time I was born, there was no way that anyone could have predicted that I would become an airplane pilot. I grew up picking cotton, but was able to go to college in Oklahoma for one year."

This is amazing, Tate thought. A lot of the people he had met so far had moved around a lot. He assumed that most people stayed where they were born. Maybe I should move sometime too. I want to be like these people and have adventures in my life.

"Where did you go after Oklahoma?" Tate needed to understand.

"I moved to Chicago and lived with my brother while working as a manicurist. During the war I used to listen to my brother and his friends talk about the bravery of the black pilots from the war. I collected pictures of airplanes and put them in the barbershop where I worked. I wanted to learn how to fly, but no school in this country would take me, because I was black and female."

"You know Tate, sometimes people had to leave this country in order to pursue their dreams. I went to England after I escaped from slavery," said Frederick Douglass.

"Yes, and I also went to England to speak about the violence that was happening in this country," said Ida B. Wells.

"In order to pursue my dream to fly I had to go to a school in France. I learned French and got my international pilot's license in 1922," said Bessie Coleman.

"Did you stay in France?" asked Tate.

"No. I came home to the United States and started doing air shows. I did a whole lot of them, but unfortunately, died in a plane crash in 1926."

"It's amazing how much influence the different wars had on our opportunities to pursue careers that we might not have otherwise had," said a man with a mustache wearing the brown suit.

"Did you fight in a war also?" asked Tate.

"No. My name is Daniel Hale Williams and I became a doctor."

"I didn't know there were black doctors way back hundreds of years ago," said Tate. "I hardly ever see any on TV or in movies or anything. How did you know you wanted to be a doctor?"

"I was always interested in science and became a doctor," said Williams. "Even though there was prejudice, I was appointed to the Illinois State Board of Health in 1889, and established Provident Hospital in Chicago and a nursing school in 1891. I also performed the first successful open heart surgery in 1893. I decided to retire in 1926 and helped establish at least 40 hospitals serving primarily black patients. I died in 1931."

17

"Wow! I had no idea there were so many people who did things to create opportunities before Dr. Martin Luther King, Jr," said Tate.

"There are thousands of people who have done all kinds of things like inventions, started businesses and schools, wrote books, made laws and fought for freedom and equality," said Booker T. Washington. "For so long, a lot of talented people made contributions to the United States. In fact, some of us actually worked together or shared ideas. I asked Marcus Garvey to visit Tuskegee Institute in 1915, but I died that year before we were able to work together."

"A lot of people were fascinated with Marcus Garvey's efforts to organize the Universal Negro Improvement Association (UNIA) and the African Communities League," said a woman wearing a pink dress.

"What's that?" Tate had never heard of the organization before.

 "The UNIA was an organization that I started in 1914," said the large man with the army looking uniform and big headdress. "Its goal was to promote racial unity through education, encourage racial pride, establish worldwide commercial activity, and develop Africa."

"Are you related to Frederick Douglass?"

"No son. My name is Marcus Garvey," he chuckled. "But like Frederick Douglass, I also spent a lot of time outside of the United States. I traveled to Central and South America in 1910," Garvey continued. "Based on the injustices I saw towards people of African descent, I wanted to have a global movement to improve lives for all people who were black."

"So, were you born a slave, too?" Tate inquired.

"No. I was actually born in St. Ann's Bay, Jamaica in 1887. I went to New York City in 1916 and recruited nearly 2,000 members to the UNIA. In order to further my work I started a weekly newspaper called *Negro World* in 1918."

"I didn't know that black people owned newspapers! I thought we only were on TV sometimes," said Tate. He couldn't believe how much he was learning from these people. He wanted to know more. "So, what happened after you started the newspaper?"

Marcus Garvey replied, "In 1920 I staged a month-long convention in Harlem, which resulted in encouraging black people from around the world to establish their own free republic of Africa. By 1921, there were over one million people throughout the United States, the West Indies, Central and South America who were part of the UNIA."

"The ideas of Marcus Garvey captured a lot of people's interest," said Ida B. Wells. "He had some great ideas, and I joined his organization called Democracy Congress and was elected to be a delegate to attend a meeting in France, but that never happened. Mr. Garvey was very instrumental in helping people across the globe feel connected to each other."

"Who knows what would have happened if my idea of building a shipping company would have actually materialized. Unfortunately, I died in 1940 after being sent back to Jamaica," said Marcus Garvey.

The woman wearing the pink dress said "I actually hosted a meeting at my home for the International League of Darker Peoples with Marcus Garvey, but I wasn't part of that group for very long."

"What's your name?" Tate couldn't help but ask.

"I'm Madam C. J. Walker," the lady replied. "We were very excited about the prospect of having such strong connections between people from all over the globe. In fact, in 1918, Ida B. Wells and I were set to go to a Peace Conference in Versailles, France with the National Equal Rights League, but we were denied passports."

"Where's Versailles?" Tate could barely pronounce the name.

"It's a city outside of Paris, France that has a famous palace."

"You were going to a palace? That's amazing! I wish I could go to a palace, too."

"Well, we never went, Tate. And remember, I didn't grow up thinking I would get invited to a palace either. I was born Sarah Breedlove, in Delta, Louisiana in 1867, just two years after slavery ended."

"Wow! So were you able to go to school also, like these other people who were born after slavery?" asked Tate.

"Well, my childhood was very difficult and I got married at an early age. I worked as a washer woman to make a living, but eventually learned about hair and scalp treatments. In 1906, I became an entrepreneur by helping black women take care of their scalps with hair ointment. I also helped create careers for saleswomen and I became a millionaire."

"You made a million dollars from helping women with their hair?" Tate was in awe.

"Yes, I helped women take care of their hair, but also helped other women become financially self-sufficient, because I provided jobs to hundreds of people, mostly women."

"Was that hard, too?"

"Doing something different than what's expected is never easy, Tate."

All of the people in the room nodded their heads in agreement.

Madam C. J. Walker continued, "I truly believed that we needed to take care of each other, and I gave some of my money to Booker T. Washington's Tuskegee Institute and the National Association for the Advancement of Colored People (NAACP), and provided some expenses for Ida B. Wells to fight against lynching. I also helped pay off the mortgage on Frederick Douglass' house. I died in 1919."

"Madam C. J. Walker, I'll always be grateful for your belief and support of my ideas. You also helped direct a fundraising drive to

 establish my school," said a brown-skinned woman with striking white hair. She was wearing a black coat and a strand of pearls. Tate was amazed at how much this lady looked like his grandmother.

"Are you and Madam C. J. Walker sisters?" asked Tate.

"No son. But we weren't born that many years apart. Madam C. J. Walker was born in 1867 in Louisiana. I was born in 1875 in South Carolina, 10 years after the Civil War ended." she replied. "My name is Mary McLeod Bethune."

"I've never seen you in any of my history books before," said Tate. "Did you become a doctor or something?"

"No Tate, I lived a poor life of struggle, but went on to become an educator and women's rights advocate," she continued. "In fact, I started Daytona Normal and Industrial School in 1904. Twenty years later it merged with a boy's school and was renamed Bethune-Cookman College."

"You started a school, too? Just like Booker T. Washington did?"

"Yes, Tate. There are a lot of us who did what needed to be done in order to give others a chance to better themselves in life. Education is the key to having choices in life," said Bethune.

"What did you do after you started the school?" asked Tate.

"In 1935, I founded the National Council of Negro Women. I lived

22

to be 80 years old and died in 1955."

"I also never experienced slavery," said a caramel-colored man with a small beard and thin mustache.

"You're W.E.B. DuBois, right?" Tate felt smart because he recognized the man.

"Yes, young man. I'm impressed that you know who I am."

"I saw you in the picture, also." Tate stared at the distinguished looking man. "I like your mustache."

"Thank you. I hope you realize that you're very lucky to be living at the time you are. I was born in Great Barrington, Massachusetts in 1868, and was able to get my education at Harvard University."

"You went to Harvard University? I didn't know that people like us went there!"

"You see, son, that's why you need to stay in school. The more you learn, the more you'll become aware of what's possible in the world. I became a writer and teacher. I was a professor at Atlanta University for almost twenty years."

Twenty years. How could anyone do the same thing for twice as long as I've been alive, thought Tate. "So, did you like teaching?" he asked.

"Yes. And I also enjoyed writing. In 1896, I published *The Suppression of the African Slave Trade* and in 1899, *The Philadelphia Negro*. One of my most famous books is *The Souls of Black Folk*, which I published in 1903. I also became the editor of the NAACP's *Crisis* magazine," W.E.B. DuBois continued. "You know, Ida B. Wells and I were both founders of the NAACP in 1909."

"You mean, you actually started an organization?" asked Tate.

"Well. There were several dozen people who started the NAACP. We had to do something to try and make life better for us. I started off thinking more moderately about how to deal with oppression and injustice, and was a little more in alignment with Booker T. Washington. But, as time went on, I became less hopeful about race relations in the United States."

"That's sad. You know, sometimes my grandmother says the same thing," Tate paused. "Did you stay working with the NAACP?"

"I worked with the NAACP for almost twenty years. But, I eventually moved to Ghana in West Africa because it was possible to live more in peace over there. I died in 1963."

"You know, Tate, there were a lot of organizations that were started by us over the years," said a clean-shaven man with a dark suit and dark tie on.

"Are you a business man?" asked Tate.

Not really in a technical sense. My name is

Carter G. Woodson. I was another person who was lucky to be born after slavery ended," he said. "I was born in 1875 – the same year as Mary McLeod Bethune - and founded the Association for the Study of Negro Life and History, along with three other men in 1915. A year later, I created the publication the *Journal of Negro History* and encouraged Mary McLeod Bethune and W.E.B. DuBois and others to write articles for it. In 1926, I started Black History Week, which later became Black History Month. I died in 1950."

"Wow," said Tate. "You mean that we didn't always have Black History Month?"

"No, son," said Carter G. Woodson. "I was the one who thought of the idea. And we decided to have it in February because that's the month that both Abraham Lincoln and Frederick Douglass have birthdays. We wanted to honor those two great men who helped end slavery."

"So, that's why you chose February? A lot of people think it's because February is the shortest month of the year," said Tate.

"Even though we had different ideas and worked in different professions, everyone in this room had a sense of hope that things could get better in this country," said the gray-haired man with large black-framed glasses.

"What did you do? I can't believe there's more," Tate was amazed.

"Oh yes. Plenty more. If you think times are hard now, you can't imagine what it was like for us. I was born in Baltimore, Maryland in 1908. My name was originally Thoroughgood Marshall, but I shortened it to Thurgood Marshall. In 1936 I began working for the NAACP. In 1938 I became head of its legal staff. I fought against legal discrimination on the now famous 1954 Brown vs. Board of Education case for the NAACP Legal Defense Fund."

"Are you serious? You mean it took a court order to make it so the schools weren't separated by race?" Tate was stunned. Wow, so many of my classmates are Mexican, Asian, white and black and have all kinds of skin colors, he thought. I never considered it to be such a big deal that my friends all look so different.

"Tate, the reason why your school is filled with people who look different is due to the court case ruling of Brown vs. Board of Education. The Supreme Court declared that schools could no longer be segregated based on race," Thurgood Marshall explained. "There was a new sense of hope that segregation and inequality would end. People truly believed that we could be a society that provided equal opportunity for all."

"But, I can go to school wherever I want," said Tate.

"That's because we continued to fight for our rights, even after the 1950s were over. I was born in Mississippi in 1925," said a man with the

slight mustache who wore a dark colored suit.

"What's your name?" Tate had no idea who the man was.

"Medgar Evers. And I worked for the NAACP like Thurgood Marshall. In fact, I was appointed field secretary after two years. Things in Mississippi were very difficult. We didn't have the right to vote and there were still many areas where we as black people didn't have the same opportunities as white people. I made speeches and led demonstrations and encouraged boycotts until I was killed in 1963."

"Isn't that the same year W.E.B. DuBois died?" asked Tate.

"Yes. Exactly. See how our work is intertwined? None of us could do what we did without the others also doing their work," said Medgar Evers.

"I was also part of the NAACP," said Rosa Parks.

"So, wait a minute," said Tate. "You mean Ida B. Wells and W.E.B. DuBois helped found the NAACP. Then, Thurgood Marshall and Medgar Evers worked for it. Madam C. J. Walker gave money to the organization. And then, the same organization helped you Mrs. Rosa Parks?"

"Yes. The NAACP helped me a lot, especially in 1955 when I refused to give up my seat on a bus in Montgomery, Alabama."

"Wow! I bet none of you could imagine that the NAACP would

be involved in boycotts for over 40 years," Tate was impressed with how many of these people were connected to the same organization.

"Probably not, young man. We never imagined the fight for equality would last so long," said Ida B. Wells. "I mean, in 1884, I sued the railroad because of discrimination. Then, almost 90 years later, in 1955, Rosa Parks was still fighting the same indignity of not being able to sit where she wanted on a bus."

"Yes. Well, thank God for the NAACP posting bond for me. And Dr. Martin Luther King, Jr. for helping to organize the bus boycott that lasted for 381 days," said Rosa Parks. "And after all of that, it still took the U.S. Supreme Court to declare Alabama laws on segregation to be unconstitutional."

"I was so young at that time," said Dr. Martin Luther King, Jr. "I was born in 1929 and studied for my doctorate at Boston University. I met Coretta Scott while I was there and we got married. Shortly after I went back home to Atlanta, I was selected to be pastor of the Dexter Avenue Baptist Church in Montgomery, Alabama in 1954. Organizing the bus boycott in Montgomery was one of the early things I did in my ministerial career. I had no idea that I was going to become a leader of the Civil Rights Movement, but did what I could to get justice in this country."

"I watched all of that non-violent movement that was taking place in the South. I just couldn't get myself to do that," said a tall man with red hair and wire-framed glasses.

Tate stared at the man and thought he looked familiar. "Are you Malcolm X?"

"Yes. I'm surprised that you know who I am. Dr. King is the one who gets taught about in school. People like his idea of non-violence, but I just didn't have the same idea about how to solve the problems in this country."

"What happened in your life to make you feel that way?" Tate couldn't help but ask.

"I was born in 1925 in Little Rock, Arkansas. My father was a strong believer in Marcus Garvey's ideas of black people having independence and self-respect. I got into some trouble in school, then later went to prison for six years. I joined the Nation of Islam in 1952 and truly believed that we needed to fight to get the rights we deserve in this country we helped build. Unfortunately, my life ended in 1965 when I was killed in the Audubon Ballroom in New York City."

"We were all shaken by the death of Malcolm X," said the Protestor who marched for equal working conditions and pay for sanitation workers in Memphis. "Dr. Martin Luther King, Jr. came to help us with our strike in 1968. That's when he got killed at the Lorraine Motel."

"1968 was a busy year because it was also the year that I was elected to Congress," said a woman with a black and white sweater and large black-framed glasses.

Tate was starting to feel overwhelmed from learning about all of these fascinating people. He had no idea who the woman was, but finally got brave enough to ask her what her name was.

"Shirley Chisholm is my name and I was the first black woman congressperson in the country," she said. "I was born in 1924, and spent my life working to make sure we progressed as a people. I actually ran for President of the United States in 1972 and I co-sponsored a bill which would create the first monument to a black person in the nation's capital. I was very proud to see the statue of Mary McLeod Bethune being unveiled on July, 19, 1974 in Lincoln Park in Washington, DC. It was the first monument to an African American or woman to be built on federal land."

"It's amazing how many things happened in such a short time," said a woman wearing a blue jacket and a strand of white pearls. "Eight years after Shirley Chisholm made history, I was able to open The Martin Luther King, Jr. National Historic Site in Atlanta, Georgia in 1981."

"What's that?" asked Tate.

"It's a national institution dedicated to the preservation of the struggles and triumphs of African Americans. I served as CEO and President."

"Who are you?" asked Tate. She did look familiar, but he wasn't sure what her name was.

"My name is Coretta Scott King and I was born in 1927. I studied music in Boston, which is where I met my husband, Dr. Martin Luther King, Jr. We had four children, all while dedicating our lives to making a better life for our children and our country. After Martin was killed, I spent my time raising my children and keeping my husband's legacy alive. I also fought many years to make my husband's birthday a national holiday. I died in 2006."

"You mean the King holiday didn't always exist?" Tate was stunned.

"No Tate. The first national Martin Luther King, Jr. holiday was observed in 1986. A lot of things that your generation takes for granted didn't exist before the 1970s. We've been fighting as a people for a long time to have equal opportunity and recognition in this country. When I was growing up, we didn't have the same rights that you have today," said Coretta Scott King.

"You mean you couldn't go out and play before you finished your homework, like me?"

Coretta Scott King laughed. "No Tate. I mean we couldn't go to the same parks, drink out of the same water fountain, go to the same schools, vote, buy property, work the same jobs or do so many of the things you can do today."

"Really? But, this is the best country in the world. Everyone has opportunities here."

"This country does have opportunities for people, whether you were born in this country or not," said a brown-skinned man with a small beard. He was wearing a cream colored jacket. Tate was struck by how fitting his jacket was. Almost everyone he knew wore clothes that were loose.

Tate was embarrassed to ask the man his name. The man could see that Tate didn't recognize him and said "My name is Jean Baptiste Point DuSable, and I was born in Haiti around 1745 and lived until 1819. There was also slavery in my home country, but I came to the United States at an early age in the late 1770s. I built a home and trading post in the city that's now called Chicago. People credit me with being the founder of Chicago."

"Wow! That's amazing," said a stout man with a big smile, salt and pepper hair, and a gray suit.

"Are you Harold Washington, the first black mayor of Chicago?" asked Tate.

"Yes. I was born in 1922 and became the first black mayor of Chicago in 1983. I tried my best to make things fair for all the citizens of Chicago. I showed everyone it was possible to build partnerships in a divided city. I was making progress, but unfortunately I only lived a little past my first term as mayor and died in 1987."

"Are you serious?" Tate was surprised that Chicago didn't have a

 black mayor until 1983.

"Did you know this country elected a black president?" Tate asked.

"Yes. I heard that a young man named Barack Hussein Obama was elected President of the United States of America in 2008," said Harold Washington. "He was born in Hawaii in 1961, but got his political experience in my hometown Chicago and the State of Illinois, first as a state senator, and then as U.S. Senator."

"Yes, things are tough because I inherited a much divided country that was in the middle of one of the worst recessions in recent history," said President Obama, who had a microphone in his hand. "But, luckily, I have all of these people who came before me who I can learn from and be inspired by. I'm the first African-American president, but I'm not the first black man to do something difficult."

"See, Tate, we have a long history of breaking barriers, defying odds, and doing things that other people find difficult," said Harold Washington.

President Barack Obama said, "Whenever I find myself wondering if I can do something, I just look in history books and learn about other people who came before me."

"Do you ever feel scared?" Tate wanted to know.

"No, Tate," said President Barack Obama. "I feel inspired because

 I know that even if my situation isn't exactly the same, there is always something I can learn from people in the past. That's why I love history and hopefully, you will love it too. History makes you feel like you're not alone even if you're the only person you personally know who's doing what you're doing."

Wow, thought Tate. Now I realize that history can help me be strong.

"Tate. Stop wasting time. Do your homework! It's almost time for dinner," his mother said.

Tate looked around and saw that he was still sitting at the kitchen table. He opened his mouth to tell his mother how he met all of these people who were in the picture, but realized that it would sound so outrageous that no one would believe him. But he was so energized that he did his homework with enthusiasm now.

"Mom! I think this is the greatest homework assignment ever," Tate said.

What has gotten into this boy, his mother wondered. "You seem interested in doing this paper now. Why the sudden enthusiasm?" she asked.

"Well mom. I feel like I met all of the people in this picture, and they told me I can be anything I want to be!"

"What do you mean you met them? How is that possible?" his mother asked.

"Well, uh…" he looked at his mother and realized there's no way she'd believe him. "Never mind. I guess I just dreamed that I met them. But, it was a cool dream."

"Okay baby. Whatever you say."

"The people in the dream were scientists, writers, civil rights activists, politicians, soldiers and all kinds of things. If they could do it, I can do it."

"That's right, Tate," his mother said. "The more you learn about what people did before you, the more you realize what's possible. History is a great source of inspiration. Who are you going to write about?"

"Wow! That's a hard choice. There are so many great stories. I can't wait to learn more. Do you think it will be okay if I write about more than one of them?" asked Tate.

"Baby, for your homework, choose one. But we can work on learning more about all of these people during your free time. The more you learn, the stronger you'll be."

Tate couldn't wait to start learning more. He got so into learning about his new heroes that his mother actually had to stop him so he could take a break and play.

Most of the historic figures included in this book are well known. There are many sources available, including books, Web sites, films, TV shows, and plays that have detailed information about them. Please feel free to use the list below to keep track of the people you research.

1. Union Soldier

2. Thurgood Marshall

3. Capt. P.B.S. Pinchback

4. George Washington Carver

5. Madam C. J. Walker

6. Mary McLeod Bethune

7. Harold Washington

8. Daniel Hale Williams

9. Rosa Parks

10. Medgar Evers

11. Sojourner Truth

12. W.E.B. DuBois

13. Union Soldier

14. Shirley Chisholm

15. Jean Baptiste Pointe DuSable

16. Bessie Coleman

17. The Protester

18. Coretta Scott King

19. Booker T. Washington

20. President Barack Obama

21. Harriet Tubman

22. Ida B. Wells

23. Marcus Garvey

24. Phillis Wheatley

25. Carter G. Woodson

26. Dr. Martin Luther King, Jr.

27. Malcolm X

28. Frederick Douglass

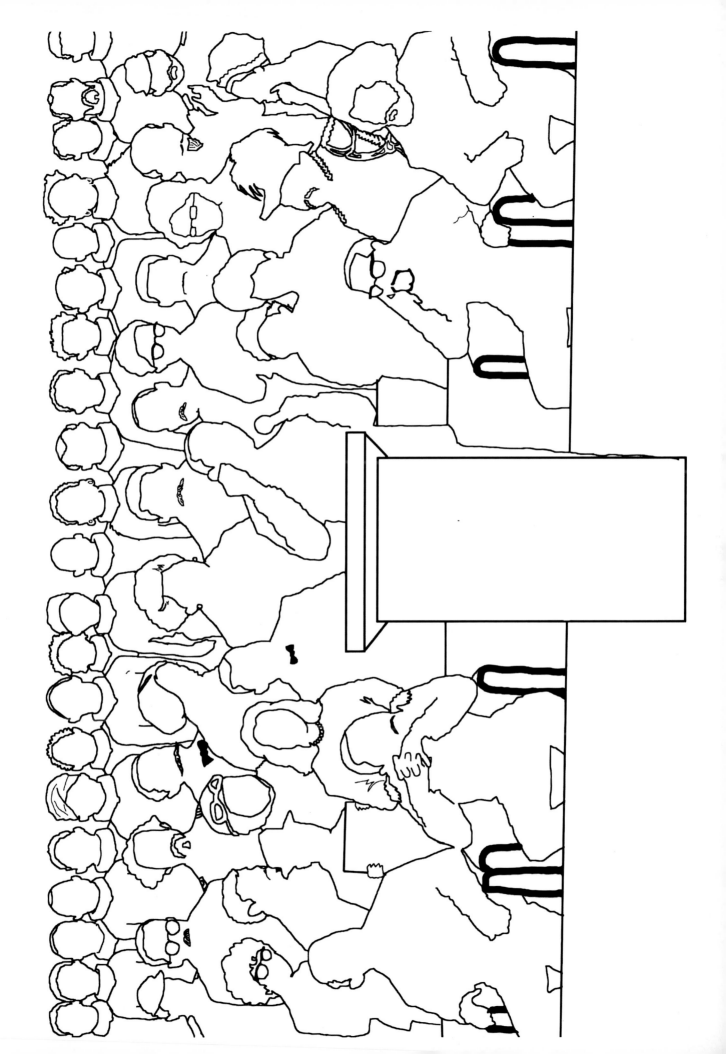

Bernard C. Turner

Bernard Turner has a career in teaching German and Spanish and a sales representative and marketing manager in educational publishing. He is a docent at the Chicago History Museum where he gives walking tours of Old Town and Lincoln Park. He also provides Green Line and Brown Line 'L' tours and guided tours of Bronzeville and other neighborhoods. In 2002, Mr. Turner founded Highlights of Chicago Press with the publication of *A View of Bronzeville*, a neighborhood tour guide that focuses on the important institutions and people that made Bronzeville a great neighborhood.

In addition to his volunteer work at the Chicago History Museum, Bernard is on the board of the Camp Douglas Restoration Foundation and The Black Metropolis National Heritage Area Commission.

Bernard studied German and History at the University of Illinois, Urbana and at the University of Chicago.

Michelle Duster

Michelle Duster is a writer, speaker, and personal historian. She has written articles, essays and compiled two books that include the original writing of her great-grandmother, Ida B. Wells – journalist, civil rights activist and suffragist: *Ida In Her Own Words* (2008) and *Ida From Abroad* (2010). She was also a contributor to the book *In Spite of the Double Drawbacks: African American Women in History and Culture* (2012) and *Women Building Chicago: 1790-1990* (2001)

A native Chicagoan, Michelle earned her B.A. in Psychology from Dartmouth College in Hanover, NH, and her M.A. in Media Studies from The New School in New York City.

Other Publications by Highlights of Chicago Press:

TJ and the Mysterious Stranger

Our Chicago—People and Places

The Windies' City—Chicago's Historical Hidden Treasures

Chicago Neighborhoods with Flavor—Getting out of the Loop

My Spanish Coloring Book

Science Makes Friends

Sam and Joe Joe's First Day